forever ella

19 Ella Fitzgerald Classics

GW00771017

Production: Sadie Cook
Cover by Watkiss Studios Limited

Published 1997

© International Music Publications Limited
Southend Road, Woodford Green, Essex IG8 8HN, England

Due to copyright restrictions *How Deep Is The Ocean?* and *Blue Skies* do not appear in this collection.

someone to watch over me

Music and Lyrics by George Gershwin and Ira Gershwin

There's a say-ing old Says that love is blind, Still we're of-ten told, "Seek and

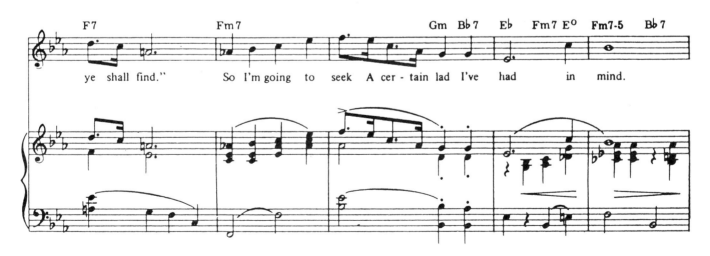

ye shall find." So I'm going to seek A cer-tain lad I've had in mind.

4

I love paris

Words and Music by Cole Porter

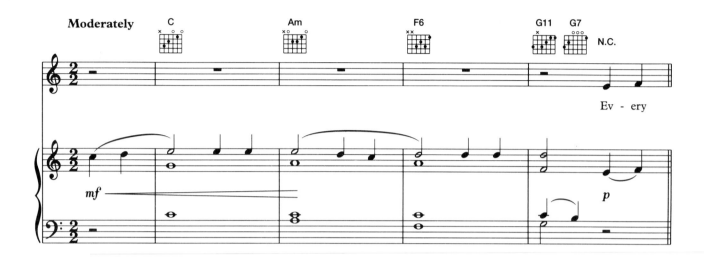

summertime

Music and Lyrics by George Gershwin,
Dubose and Dorothy Heyward and Ira Gershwin

there's a - no - thin' can harm you, with dad - dy an' mam - my stand - in' by.

misty

Words by Johnny Burke
Music by Errol Garner

gone with the wind

Words and Music by Herbert Magdison and Allie Wrubel

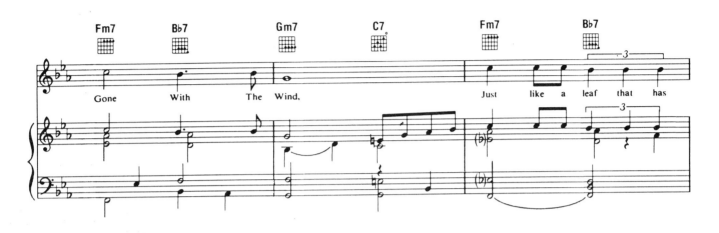

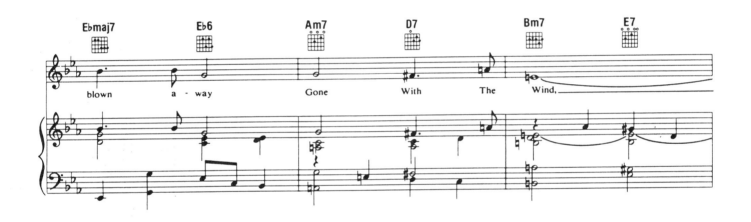

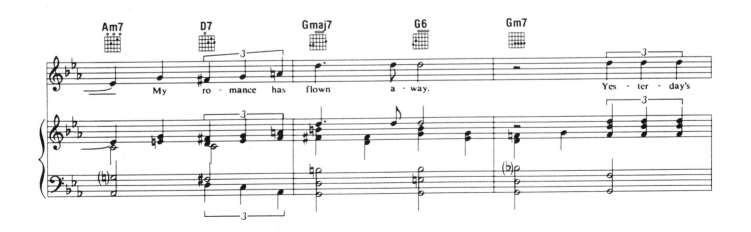

I can't give you anything but love

Words by Dorothy Fields
Music by Jimmy McHugh

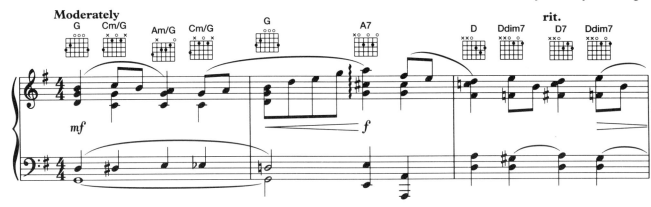

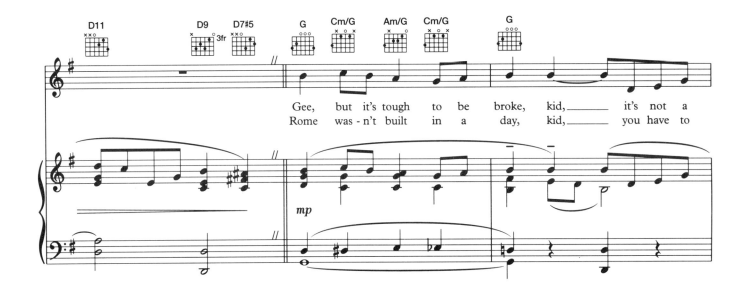

Gee, but it's tough to be broke, kid,_____ it's not a
Rome was-n't built in a day, kid,_____ you have to

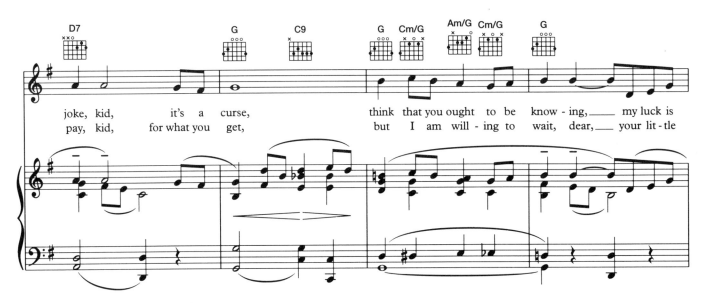

joke, kid,   it's a curse,   think that you ought to be know-ing,_____ my luck is
pay, kid,   for what you   get,   but I am will-ing to wait, dear,_____ your lit-tle

go - ing_____ from bad to worse. Who knows, some-day I will

mate, dear,_____ will not for - get. You have a life - time be -

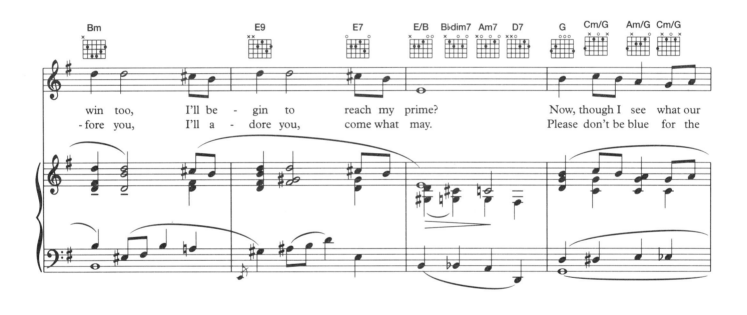

win too, I'll be - gin to reach my prime? Now, though I see what our

-fore you, I'll a - dore you, come what may. Please don't be blue for the

end is,_____ all I can spend is just my time.

pre - sent,_____ when it's so plea - sant to hear you say:

poco rall.

tenderly

Words by Jack Lawrence
Music by Walter Gross

I only have eyes for you

Words by Al Dubin
Music by Harry Warren

Moderately

Are the stars out to-night?_____ I don't know if it's clou-dy or

bright,_____ 'cause I on-ly have eyes_____ for

you,_____ dear._____ The moon may be high,_____ but I

love me or leave me

Words by Gus Kahn
Music by Walter Donaldson

30

these foolish things

Words and Music by Harry Link,
Jack Strachey and Holt Marvell

36

the very thought of you

Words and Music by Ray Noble

39

40

you do something to me

Words and Music by Cole Porter

well, for you do

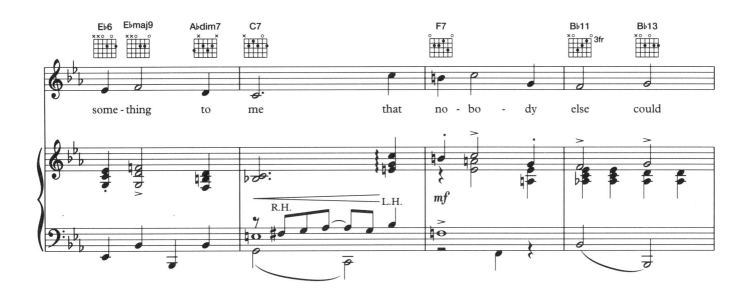

some-thing to me that no-bo-dy else could

do! do!

I won't dance

Words by Oscar Hammerstein II, Dorothy Fields,
Otto Harbach and Jimmy McHugh
Music by Jerome Kern

48

mountain greenery

Words by Lorenz Hart
Music by Richard Rodgers

52

54

I've got my love to keep me warm

Words and Music by Irving Berlin

lullaby of birdland

Words by George David Weiss
Music by George Shearing

on the sunny side of the street

Words by Dorothy Fields
Music by Jimmy McHugh

I get a kick out of you

Words and Music by Cole Porter

one for my baby
(and one more for the road)

Words by Johnny Mercer
Music by Harold Arlen

73

74

The W All oman Series

W All oman
volume one

Contents include: All Woman; Do You Know Where You're Going To?; Ev'ry Time We Say Goodbye;
Fever; I Am What I Am; I Will Always Love You; Miss You Like Crazy; Summertime;
Superwoman; What's Love Got To Do With It and Why Do Fools Fall In Love.
Order Ref: 19076

W All oman
volume two

Contents include: Don't It Make My Brown Eyes Blue; Giving You The Best That I Got;
Killing Me Softly With His Song; Memory; One Moment In Time; Pearl's A Singer;
That Ole Devil Called Love; Walk On By; The Wind Beneath My Wings and You Don't Have To Say You Love Me.
Order Ref: 2043A

W All oman
volume three

Contents include: Almaz; Big Spender; Crazy For You; Fame; The First Time Ever I Saw Your Face;
From A Distance; Love Letters; My Baby Just Cares For Me; My Funny Valentine; The Power Of Love;
Promise Me; Saving All My Love For You and Total Eclipse Of The Heart.
Order Ref: 2444A

W All oman
volume four

Contents include: Anything For You; Evergreen; For Your Eyes Only; I Will Survive; Mad About The Boy;
A Rainy Night in Georgia; Send In The Clowns; Smooth Operator; Sophisticated Lady; Stay With Me Till Dawn;
Sweet Love; Think Twice and Touch Me In The Morning.
Order Ref: 3034A

W All oman
Blues

Contents include: Body and Soul; Georgia On My Mind; God Bless' The Child;
I Don't Stand A Ghost Of A Chance With You; I Gotta Right To Sing The Blues; I'd Rather Go Blind;
Lover Man (Oh, Where Can You Be?); Mood Indigo; Stormy Weather and You've Changed.
Order Ref: 3690A

W All oman
Cabaret

Contents include: Almost Like Being In Love; Another Openin', Another Show; Anything Goes;
For Once In My Life; Goldfinger; I Won't Last A Day Without You; If My Friends Could See Me Now;
My Way; New York New York; People and There's No Business Like Show Business.
Order Ref: 3691A

W All oman
Jazz

Contents include: Bewitched; Crazy He Calls Me; A Foggy Day; Girl From Ipanema; How High The Moon;
I'm In The Mood For Love; It Don't Mean A Thing (If It Ain't Got That Swing); It's Only A Paper Moon;
Misty; On Green Dolphin Street; 'Round Midnight and Straighten Up And Fly Right.
Order Ref: 4778A